In celebration of

Date

GUEST

NAME _____

ADDRESS _____

PREDICTIONS FOR BABY ARE:

DATE OF BIRTH WILL BE _____

TIME OF BIRTH WILL BE _____

WEIGHT OF BABY _____

EYES COLOR WILL BE _____

MOST LIKE MOM OR DAD _____

NAME PREDICTIONS ARE

_____

_____

DRAW THE BABY

CAN YOU GUESS WHAT THE BABY IS GOING TO LOOK LIKE?

 ## ADVICE FOR PARENTS

_____

_____

_____

WISHES FOR BABY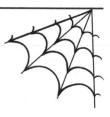

_____

_____

_____

GUEST

NAME _____

ADDRESS _____

PREDICTIONS FOR BABY ARE:

DATE OF BIRTH WILL BE _____

TIME OF BIRTH WILL BE _____

WEIGHT OF BABY _____

EYES COLOR WILL BE _____

MOST LIKE MOM OR DAD _____

NAME PREDICTIONS ARE

_____

_____

DRAW THE BABY

CAN YOU GUESS WHAT THE BABY IS GOING TO LOOK LIKE?

 # ADVICE FOR PARENTS

_____

_____

_____

WISHES FOR BABY

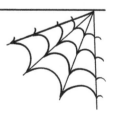

_____

_____

_____

GUEST

NAME _____

ADDRESS _____

PREDICTIONS FOR BABY ARE:

DATE OF BIRTH WILL BE _____

TIME OF BIRTH WILL BE _____

WEIGHT OF BABY _____

EYES COLOR WILL BE _____

MOST LIKE MOM OR DAD _____

NAME PREDICTIONS ARE

_____

_____

DRAW THE BABY

CAN YOU GUESS WHAT THE BABY IS GOING TO LOOK LIKE?

 ADVICE FOR PARENTS

_____

_____

_____

WISHES FOR BABY

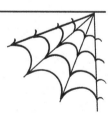

_____

_____

_____

GUEST

NAME _____

ADDRESS _____

PREDICTIONS FOR BABY ARE:

DATE OF BIRTH WILL BE _____

TIME OF BIRTH WILL BE _____

WEIGHT OF BABY _____

EYES COLOR WILL BE_____

MOST LIKE MOM OR DAD_____

NAME PREDICTIONS ARE

_____

_____

DRAW THE BABY

CAN YOU GUESS WHAT
THE BABY IS GOING TO
LOOK LIKE?

 # ADVICE FOR PARENTS

_____

_____

_____

WISHES FOR BABY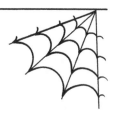

_____

_____

_____

GUEST

NAME _____

ADDRESS _____

PREDICTIONS FOR BABY ARE:

DATE OF BIRTH WILL BE _____

TIME OF BIRTH WILL BE _____

WEIGHT OF BABY _____

EYES COLOR WILL BE _____

MOST LIKE MOM OR DAD _____

NAME PREDICTIONS ARE

_____

_____

DRAW THE BABY

CAN YOU GUESS WHAT THE BABY IS GOING TO LOOK LIKE?

 ADVICE FOR PARENTS

_____

_____

_____

WISHES FOR BABY

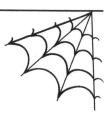

_____

_____

_____

GUEST

NAME _____

ADDRESS _____

PREDICTIONS FOR BABY ARE:

DATE OF BIRTH WILL BE _____

TIME OF BIRTH WILL BE _____

WEIGHT OF BABY _____

EYES COLOR WILL BE _____

MOST LIKE MOM OR DAD _____

NAME PREDICTIONS ARE

_____

_____

DRAW THE BABY

CAN YOU GUESS WHAT
THE BABY IS GOING TO
LOOK LIKE?

 # ADVICE FOR PARENTS

_____

_____

WISHES FOR BABY

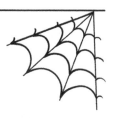

_____

_____

_____

GUEST

NAME _____

ADDRESS _____

PREDICTIONS FOR BABY ARE:

DATE OF BIRTH WILL BE _____

TIME OF BIRTH WILL BE _____

WEIGHT OF BABY _____

EYES COLOR WILL BE _____

MOST LIKE MOM OR DAD _____

NAME PREDICTIONS ARE

_____

_____

DRAW THE BABY

CAN YOU GUESS WHAT THE BABY IS GOING TO LOOK LIKE?

 # ADVICE FOR PARENTS

_____

_____

_____

WISHES FOR BABY

_____

_____

_____

GUEST

NAME _____

ADDRESS _____

PREDICTIONS FOR BABY ARE:

DATE OF BIRTH WILL BE _____

TIME OF BIRTH WILL BE _____

WEIGHT OF BABY _____

EYES COLOR WILL BE _____

MOST LIKE MOM OR DAD _____

NAME PREDICTIONS ARE

_____

_____

DRAW THE BABY

CAN YOU GUESS WHAT THE BABY IS GOING TO LOOK LIKE?

 # ADVICE FOR PARENTS

_____

_____

_____

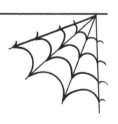

WISHES FOR BABY

_____

_____

_____

_____

GUEST

NAME _____

ADDRESS _____

PREDICTIONS FOR BABY ARE:

DATE OF BIRTH WILL BE _____

TIME OF BIRTH WILL BE _____

WEIGHT OF BABY _____

EYES COLOR WILL BE _____

MOST LIKE MOM OR DAD _____

NAME PREDICTIONS ARE

_____

_____

DRAW THE BABY

CAN YOU GUESS WHAT THE BABY IS GOING TO LOOK LIKE?

 # ADVICE FOR PARENTS

_____

_____

_____

WISHES FOR BABY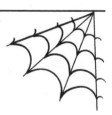

_____

_____

_____

GUEST

NAME _____

ADDRESS _____

PREDICTIONS FOR BABY ARE:

DATE OF BIRTH WILL BE _____

TIME OF BIRTH WILL BE _____

WEIGHT OF BABY _____

EYES COLOR WILL BE _____

MOST LIKE MOM OR DAD _____

NAME PREDICTIONS ARE

_____

_____

DRAW THE BABY

CAN YOU GUESS WHAT THE BABY IS GOING TO LOOK LIKE?

 ADVICE FOR PARENTS

_____

_____

_____

WISHES FOR BABY

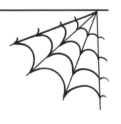

_____

_____

_____

GUEST

NAME _____

ADDRESS _____

PREDICTIONS FOR BABY ARE:

DATE OF BIRTH WILL BE _____

TIME OF BIRTH WILL BE _____

WEIGHT OF BABY _____

EYES COLOR WILL BE _____

MOST LIKE MOM OR DAD _____

NAME PREDICTIONS ARE

_____

_____

DRAW THE BABY

CAN YOU GUESS WHAT THE BABY IS GOING TO LOOK LIKE?

 ADVICE FOR PARENTS

_____

_____

_____

WISHES FOR BABY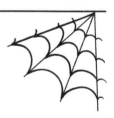

_____

_____

_____

GUEST

NAME _____

ADDRESS _____

PREDICTIONS FOR BABY ARE:

DATE OF BIRTH WILL BE _____

TIME OF BIRTH WILL BE _____

WEIGHT OF BABY _____

EYES COLOR WILL BE _____

MOST LIKE MOM OR DAD _____

NAME PREDICTIONS ARE

_____

_____

DRAW THE BABY

CAN YOU GUESS WHAT THE BABY IS GOING TO LOOK LIKE?

 ## ADVICE FOR PARENTS

_____

_____

_____

WISHES FOR BABY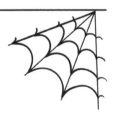

_____

_____

_____

GUEST

NAME _____

ADDRESS _____

PREDICTIONS FOR BABY ARE:

DATE OF BIRTH WILL BE _____

TIME OF BIRTH WILL BE _____

WEIGHT OF BABY _____

EYES COLOR WILL BE _____

MOST LIKE MOM OR DAD _____

NAME PREDICTIONS ARE

_____

_____

DRAW THE BABY

CAN YOU GUESS WHAT THE BABY IS GOING TO LOOK LIKE?

 # ADVICE FOR PARENTS

_____

_____

WISHES FOR BABY

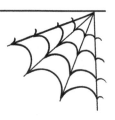

_____

_____

_____

GUEST

NAME _____

ADDRESS _____

PREDICTIONS FOR BABY ARE:

DATE OF BIRTH WILL BE _____

TIME OF BIRTH WILL BE _____

WEIGHT OF BABY _____

EYES COLOR WILL BE _____

MOST LIKE MOM OR DAD _____

NAME PREDICTIONS ARE

_____

_____

DRAW THE BABY

CAN YOU GUESS WHAT THE BABY IS GOING TO LOOK LIKE?

 # ADVICE FOR PARENTS

_____

_____

WISHES FOR BABY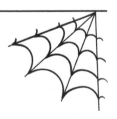

_____

_____

_____

GUEST

NAME _____

ADDRESS _____

PREDICTIONS FOR BABY ARE:

DATE OF BIRTH WILL BE _____

TIME OF BIRTH WILL BE _____

WEIGHT OF BABY _____

EYES COLOR WILL BE _____

MOST LIKE MOM OR DAD _____

NAME PREDICTIONS ARE

_____

_____

DRAW THE BABY

CAN YOU GUESS WHAT THE BABY IS GOING TO LOOK LIKE?

 # ADVICE FOR PARENTS

_____

_____

_____

WISHES FOR BABY

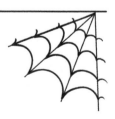

_____

_____

_____

GUEST

NAME _____

ADDRESS _____

PREDICTIONS FOR BABY ARE:

DATE OF BIRTH WILL BE _____

TIME OF BIRTH WILL BE _____

WEIGHT OF BABY _____

EYES COLOR WILL BE _____

MOST LIKE MOM OR DAD _____

NAME PREDICTIONS ARE

_____

_____

DRAW THE BABY

CAN YOU GUESS WHAT THE BABY IS GOING TO LOOK LIKE?

 ADVICE FOR PARENTS

_____

_____

_____

WISHES FOR BABY

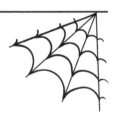

_____

_____

_____

GUEST

NAME _____

ADDRESS _____

PREDICTIONS FOR BABY ARE:

DATE OF BIRTH WILL BE _____

TIME OF BIRTH WILL BE _____

WEIGHT OF BABY _____

EYES COLOR WILL BE _____

MOST LIKE MOM OR DAD _____

NAME PREDICTIONS ARE

_____

_____

DRAW THE BABY

CAN YOU GUESS WHAT THE BABY IS GOING TO LOOK LIKE?

 # ADVICE FOR PARENTS

_____

_____

_____

WISHES FOR BABY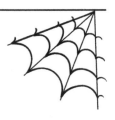

_____

_____

_____

GUEST

NAME _____

ADDRESS _____

PREDICTIONS FOR BABY ARE:

DATE OF BIRTH WILL BE _____

TIME OF BIRTH WILL BE _____

WEIGHT OF BABY _____

EYES COLOR WILL BE _____

MOST LIKE MOM OR DAD _____

NAME PREDICTIONS ARE

_____

_____

DRAW THE BABY

CAN YOU GUESS WHAT THE BABY IS GOING TO LOOK LIKE?

ADVICE FOR PARENTS

_____

_____

_____

WISHES FOR BABY

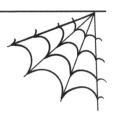

_____

_____

_____

GUEST

NAME _____

ADDRESS _____

PREDICTIONS FOR BABY ARE:

DATE OF BIRTH WILL BE _____

TIME OF BIRTH WILL BE _____

WEIGHT OF BABY _____

EYES COLOR WILL BE_____

MOST LIKE MOM OR DAD_____

NAME PREDICTIONS ARE

_____

_____

DRAW THE BABY

CAN YOU GUESS WHAT THE BABY IS GOING TO LOOK LIKE?

 ADVICE FOR PARENTS

_____

_____

_____

WISHES FOR BABY

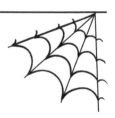

_____

_____

_____

GUEST

NAME _____

ADDRESS _____

PREDICTIONS FOR BABY ARE:

DATE OF BIRTH WILL BE _____

TIME OF BIRTH WILL BE _____

WEIGHT OF BABY _____

EYES COLOR WILL BE _____

MOST LIKE MOM OR DAD _____

NAME PREDICTIONS ARE

_____

_____

DRAW THE BABY

CAN YOU GUESS WHAT THE BABY IS GOING TO LOOK LIKE?

 # ADVICE FOR PARENTS

_____

_____

WISHES FOR BABY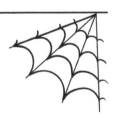

_____

_____

_____

GUEST

NAME _____

ADDRESS _____

PREDICTIONS FOR BABY ARE:

DATE OF BIRTH WILL BE _____

TIME OF BIRTH WILL BE _____

WEIGHT OF BABY _____

EYES COLOR WILL BE_____

MOST LIKE MOM OR DAD_____

NAME PREDICTIONS ARE

_____

_____

DRAW THE BABY

CAN YOU GUESS WHAT THE BABY IS GOING TO LOOK LIKE?

 ## ADVICE FOR PARENTS

_____

_____

_____

WISHES FOR BABY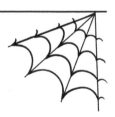

_____

_____

_____

GUEST

NAME _____

ADDRESS _____

PREDICTIONS FOR BABY ARE:

DATE OF BIRTH WILL BE _____

TIME OF BIRTH WILL BE _____

WEIGHT OF BABY _____

EYES COLOR WILL BE _____

MOST LIKE MOM OR DAD _____

NAME PREDICTIONS ARE

_____

_____

DRAW THE BABY

CAN YOU GUESS WHAT THE BABY IS GOING TO LOOK LIKE?

 ADVICE FOR PARENTS

_____

_____

_____

WISHES FOR BABY

_____

_____

_____

GUEST

NAME _____

ADDRESS _____

PREDICTIONS FOR BABY ARE:

DATE OF BIRTH WILL BE _____

TIME OF BIRTH WILL BE _____

WEIGHT OF BABY _____

EYES COLOR WILL BE _____

MOST LIKE MOM OR DAD _____

NAME PREDICTIONS ARE

_____

_____

DRAW THE BABY

CAN YOU GUESS WHAT THE BABY IS GOING TO LOOK LIKE?

 ADVICE FOR PARENTS

_____

_____

_____

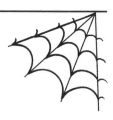

WISHES FOR BABY

_____

_____

_____

GUEST

NAME _____

ADDRESS _____

PREDICTIONS FOR BABY ARE:

DATE OF BIRTH WILL BE _____

TIME OF BIRTH WILL BE _____

WEIGHT OF BABY _____

EYES COLOR WILL BE _____

MOST LIKE MOM OR DAD _____

NAME PREDICTIONS ARE

_____

_____

DRAW THE BABY

CAN YOU GUESS WHAT THE BABY IS GOING TO LOOK LIKE?

 ADVICE FOR PARENTS

_____

_____

_____

WISHES FOR BABY

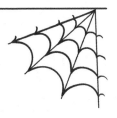

_____

_____

_____

GUEST

NAME _____

ADDRESS _____

PREDICTIONS FOR BABY ARE:

DATE OF BIRTH WILL BE _____

TIME OF BIRTH WILL BE _____

WEIGHT OF BABY _____

EYES COLOR WILL BE _____

MOST LIKE MOM OR DAD _____

NAME PREDICTIONS ARE

_____

_____

DRAW THE BABY

CAN YOU GUESS WHAT THE BABY IS GOING TO LOOK LIKE?

 ## ADVICE FOR PARENTS

_____

_____

_____

WISHES FOR BABY

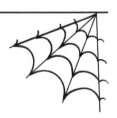

_____

_____

_____

GUEST

NAME _____

ADDRESS _____

PREDICTIONS FOR BABY ARE:

DATE OF BIRTH WILL BE _____

TIME OF BIRTH WILL BE _____

WEIGHT OF BABY _____

EYES COLOR WILL BE _____

MOST LIKE MOM OR DAD _____

NAME PREDICTIONS ARE

_____

_____

DRAW THE BABY

CAN YOU GUESS WHAT THE BABY IS GOING TO LOOK LIKE?

ADVICE FOR PARENTS

_____

_____

WISHES FOR BABY

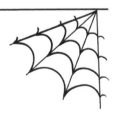

_____

_____

GUEST

NAME _____

ADDRESS _____

PREDICTIONS FOR BABY ARE:

DATE OF BIRTH WILL BE _____

TIME OF BIRTH WILL BE _____

WEIGHT OF BABY _____

EYES COLOR WILL BE _____

MOST LIKE MOM OR DAD _____

NAME PREDICTIONS ARE

_____

_____

DRAW THE BABY

CAN YOU GUESS WHAT THE BABY IS GOING TO LOOK LIKE?

 ## ADVICE FOR PARENTS

_____

_____

_____

WISHES FOR BABY

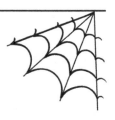

_____

_____

_____

GUEST

NAME _____

ADDRESS _____

PREDICTIONS FOR BABY ARE:

DATE OF BIRTH WILL BE _____

TIME OF BIRTH WILL BE _____

WEIGHT OF BABY _____

EYES COLOR WILL BE _____

MOST LIKE MOM OR DAD _____

NAME PREDICTIONS ARE

_____

_____

DRAW THE BABY

CAN YOU GUESS WHAT THE BABY IS GOING TO LOOK LIKE?

ADVICE FOR PARENTS

_____

_____

_____

WISHES FOR BABY
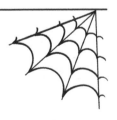

_____

_____

_____

GUEST

NAME _____

ADDRESS _____

PREDICTIONS FOR BABY ARE:

DATE OF BIRTH WILL BE _____

TIME OF BIRTH WILL BE _____

WEIGHT OF BABY _____

EYES COLOR WILL BE _____

MOST LIKE MOM OR DAD _____

NAME PREDICTIONS ARE

_____

_____

DRAW THE BABY

CAN YOU GUESS WHAT THE BABY IS GOING TO LOOK LIKE?

 # ADVICE FOR PARENTS

_____

_____

_____

WISHES FOR BABY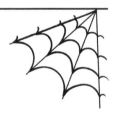

_____

_____

_____

GUEST

NAME _____

ADDRESS _____

PREDICTIONS FOR BABY ARE:

DATE OF BIRTH WILL BE _____

TIME OF BIRTH WILL BE _____

WEIGHT OF BABY _____

EYES COLOR WILL BE _____

MOST LIKE MOM OR DAD _____

NAME PREDICTIONS ARE

_____

_____

DRAW THE BABY

CAN YOU GUESS WHAT THE BABY IS GOING TO LOOK LIKE?

 ## ADVICE FOR PARENTS

_____

_____

_____

WISHES FOR BABY

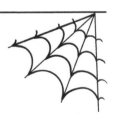

_____

_____

_____

GUEST

NAME _____

ADDRESS _____

PREDICTIONS FOR BABY ARE:

DATE OF BIRTH WILL BE _____

TIME OF BIRTH WILL BE _____

WEIGHT OF BABY _____

EYES COLOR WILL BE _____

MOST LIKE MOM OR DAD _____

NAME PREDICTIONS ARE

_____

_____

DRAW THE BABY

CAN YOU GUESS WHAT THE BABY IS GOING TO LOOK LIKE?

 ## ADVICE FOR PARENTS

_____

_____

_____

WISHES FOR BABY
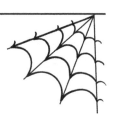

_____

_____

_____

GUEST

NAME _____

ADDRESS _____

PREDICTIONS FOR BABY ARE:

DATE OF BIRTH WILL BE _____

TIME OF BIRTH WILL BE _____

WEIGHT OF BABY _____

EYES COLOR WILL BE _____

MOST LIKE MOM OR DAD _____

NAME PREDICTIONS ARE

_____

_____

DRAW THE BABY

CAN YOU GUESS WHAT THE BABY IS GOING TO LOOK LIKE?

 ## ADVICE FOR PARENTS

_____

_____

_____

WISHES FOR BABY

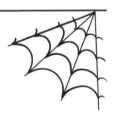

_____

_____

_____

GUEST

NAME _____

ADDRESS _____

PREDICTIONS FOR BABY ARE:

DATE OF BIRTH WILL BE _____

TIME OF BIRTH WILL BE _____

WEIGHT OF BABY _____

EYES COLOR WILL BE _____

MOST LIKE MOM OR DAD _____

NAME PREDICTIONS ARE

_____

_____

DRAW THE BABY

CAN YOU GUESS WHAT THE BABY IS GOING TO LOOK LIKE?

 # ADVICE FOR PARENTS

_____

_____

_____

WISHES FOR BABY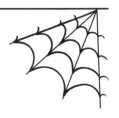

_____

_____

_____

GUEST

NAME _____

ADDRESS _____

PREDICTIONS FOR BABY ARE:

DATE OF BIRTH WILL BE _____

TIME OF BIRTH WILL BE _____

WEIGHT OF BABY _____

EYES COLOR WILL BE _____

MOST LIKE MOM OR DAD _____

NAME PREDICTIONS ARE

_____

_____

DRAW THE BABY

CAN YOU GUESS WHAT THE BABY IS GOING TO LOOK LIKE?

 # ADVICE FOR PARENTS

_____

_____

_____

WISHES FOR BABY

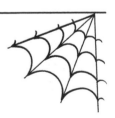

_____

_____

_____

GUEST

NAME _____

ADDRESS _____

PREDICTIONS FOR BABY ARE:

DATE OF BIRTH WILL BE _____

TIME OF BIRTH WILL BE _____

WEIGHT OF BABY _____

EYES COLOR WILL BE _____

MOST LIKE MOM OR DAD _____

NAME PREDICTIONS ARE

_____

_____

DRAW THE BABY

CAN YOU GUESS WHAT THE BABY IS GOING TO LOOK LIKE?

 ## ADVICE FOR PARENTS

_____

_____

_____

WISHES FOR BABY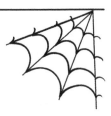

_____

_____

_____

GUEST

NAME _____

ADDRESS _____

PREDICTIONS FOR BABY ARE:

DATE OF BIRTH WILL BE _____

TIME OF BIRTH WILL BE _____

WEIGHT OF BABY _____

EYES COLOR WILL BE _____

MOST LIKE MOM OR DAD _____

NAME PREDICTIONS ARE

_____

_____

DRAW THE BABY

CAN YOU GUESS WHAT
THE BABY IS GOING TO
LOOK LIKE?

ADVICE FOR PARENTS

_____

_____

_____

WISHES FOR BABY

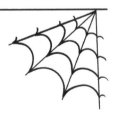

_____

_____

_____

GUEST

NAME _____

ADDRESS _____

PREDICTIONS FOR BABY ARE:

DATE OF BIRTH WILL BE _____

TIME OF BIRTH WILL BE _____

WEIGHT OF BABY _____

EYES COLOR WILL BE _____

MOST LIKE MOM OR DAD _____

NAME PREDICTIONS ARE

_____

_____

DRAW THE BABY

CAN YOU GUESS WHAT THE BABY IS GOING TO LOOK LIKE?

 ADVICE FOR PARENTS

_____

_____

_____

WISHES FOR BABY

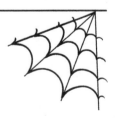

_____

_____

_____

GUEST

NAME _____

ADDRESS _____

PREDICTIONS FOR BABY ARE:

DATE OF BIRTH WILL BE _____

TIME OF BIRTH WILL BE _____

WEIGHT OF BABY _____

EYES COLOR WILL BE _____

MOST LIKE MOM OR DAD _____

NAME PREDICTIONS ARE

_____

_____

DRAW THE BABY

CAN YOU GUESS WHAT THE BABY IS GOING TO LOOK LIKE?

 # ADVICE FOR PARENTS

_____

_____

_____

WISHES FOR BABY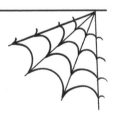

_____

_____

_____

GUEST

NAME _____

ADDRESS _____

PREDICTIONS FOR BABY ARE:

DATE OF BIRTH WILL BE _____

TIME OF BIRTH WILL BE _____

WEIGHT OF BABY _____

EYES COLOR WILL BE _____

MOST LIKE MOM OR DAD _____

NAME PREDICTIONS ARE

_____

_____

DRAW THE BABY

CAN YOU GUESS WHAT THE BABY IS GOING TO LOOK LIKE?

 # ADVICE FOR PARENTS

_____

_____

_____

WISHES FOR BABY

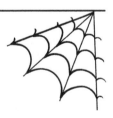

_____

_____

_____

GUEST

NAME _____

ADDRESS _____

PREDICTIONS FOR BABY ARE:

DATE OF BIRTH WILL BE _____

TIME OF BIRTH WILL BE _____

WEIGHT OF BABY _____

EYES COLOR WILL BE _____

MOST LIKE MOM OR DAD _____

NAME PREDICTIONS ARE

_____

_____

DRAW THE BABY

CAN YOU GUESS WHAT THE BABY IS GOING TO LOOK LIKE?

ADVICE FOR PARENTS

_____

_____

_____

WISHES FOR BABY

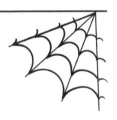

_____

_____

_____

GUEST

NAME _____

ADDRESS _____

PREDICTIONS FOR BABY ARE:

DATE OF BIRTH WILL BE _____

TIME OF BIRTH WILL BE _____

WEIGHT OF BABY _____

EYES COLOR WILL BE _____

MOST LIKE MOM OR DAD _____

NAME PREDICTIONS ARE

_____

_____

DRAW THE BABY

CAN YOU GUESS WHAT THE BABY IS GOING TO LOOK LIKE?

 # ADVICE FOR PARENTS

_____

_____

_____

WISHES FOR BABY

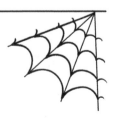

_____

_____

_____

GUEST

NAME _____

ADDRESS _____

PREDICTIONS FOR BABY ARE:

DATE OF BIRTH WILL BE _____

TIME OF BIRTH WILL BE _____

WEIGHT OF BABY _____

EYES COLOR WILL BE _____

MOST LIKE MOM OR DAD _____

NAME PREDICTIONS ARE

_____

_____

DRAW THE BABY

CAN YOU GUESS WHAT THE BABY IS GOING TO LOOK LIKE?

ADVICE FOR PARENTS

_____

_____

_____

WISHES FOR BABY

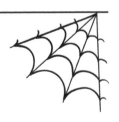

_____

_____

_____

GUEST

NAME _____

ADDRESS _____

PREDICTIONS FOR BABY ARE:

DATE OF BIRTH WILL BE _____

TIME OF BIRTH WILL BE _____

WEIGHT OF BABY _____

EYES COLOR WILL BE _____

MOST LIKE MOM OR DAD _____

NAME PREDICTIONS ARE

_____

_____

DRAW THE BABY

CAN YOU GUESS WHAT THE BABY IS GOING TO LOOK LIKE?

 ADVICE FOR PARENTS

_____

_____

_____

WISHES FOR BABY

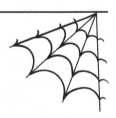

_____

_____

_____

GUEST

NAME _____

ADDRESS _____

PREDICTIONS FOR BABY ARE:

DATE OF BIRTH WILL BE _____

TIME OF BIRTH WILL BE _____

WEIGHT OF BABY _____

EYES COLOR WILL BE _____

MOST LIKE MOM OR DAD _____

NAME PREDICTIONS ARE

_____

_____

DRAW THE BABY

CAN YOU GUESS WHAT
THE BABY IS GOING TO
LOOK LIKE?

 # ADVICE FOR PARENTS

_____

_____

_____

WISHES FOR BABY

_____

_____

_____

GUEST

NAME _____

ADDRESS _____

PREDICTIONS FOR BABY ARE:

DATE OF BIRTH WILL BE _____

TIME OF BIRTH WILL BE _____

WEIGHT OF BABY _____

EYES COLOR WILL BE _____

MOST LIKE MOM OR DAD _____

NAME PREDICTIONS ARE

_____

_____

DRAW THE BABY

CAN YOU GUESS WHAT THE BABY IS GOING TO LOOK LIKE?

 # ADVICE FOR PARENTS

_____

_____

_____

WISHES FOR BABY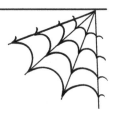

_____

_____

_____

GUEST

NAME _____

ADDRESS _____

PREDICTIONS FOR BABY ARE:

DATE OF BIRTH WILL BE _____

TIME OF BIRTH WILL BE _____

WEIGHT OF BABY _____

EYES COLOR WILL BE _____

MOST LIKE MOM OR DAD _____

NAME PREDICTIONS ARE

_____

_____

DRAW THE BABY

CAN YOU GUESS WHAT THE BABY IS GOING TO LOOK LIKE?

ADVICE FOR PARENTS

_____

_____

_____

WISHES FOR BABY

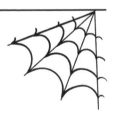

_____

_____

_____

GUEST

NAME _____

ADDRESS _____

PREDICTIONS FOR BABY ARE:

DATE OF BIRTH WILL BE _____

TIME OF BIRTH WILL BE _____

WEIGHT OF BABY _____

EYES COLOR WILL BE _____

MOST LIKE MOM OR DAD _____

NAME PREDICTIONS ARE

_____

_____

DRAW THE BABY

CAN YOU GUESS WHAT THE BABY IS GOING TO LOOK LIKE?

 # ADVICE FOR PARENTS

_____

_____

_____

WISHES FOR BABY

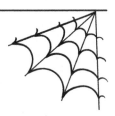

_____

_____

_____

GUEST

NAME _____

ADDRESS _____

PREDICTIONS FOR BABY ARE:

DATE OF BIRTH WILL BE _____

TIME OF BIRTH WILL BE _____

WEIGHT OF BABY _____

EYES COLOR WILL BE _____

MOST LIKE MOM OR DAD _____

NAME PREDICTIONS ARE

_____

_____

DRAW THE BABY

CAN YOU GUESS WHAT THE BABY IS GOING TO LOOK LIKE?

 ## ADVICE FOR PARENTS

_____

_____

_____

WISHES FOR BABY

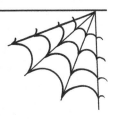

_____

_____

_____

GUEST

NAME _____

ADDRESS _____

PREDICTIONS FOR BABY ARE:

DATE OF BIRTH WILL BE _____

TIME OF BIRTH WILL BE _____

WEIGHT OF BABY _____

EYES COLOR WILL BE _____

MOST LIKE MOM OR DAD _____

NAME PREDICTIONS ARE

_____

_____

DRAW THE BABY

CAN YOU GUESS WHAT THE BABY IS GOING TO LOOK LIKE?

 ADVICE FOR PARENTS

_____

_____

_____

WISHES FOR BABY
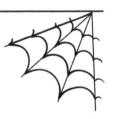

_____

_____

_____

GUEST

NAME _____

ADDRESS _____

PREDICTIONS FOR BABY ARE:

DATE OF BIRTH WILL BE _____

TIME OF BIRTH WILL BE _____

WEIGHT OF BABY _____

EYES COLOR WILL BE _____

MOST LIKE MOM OR DAD _____

NAME PREDICTIONS ARE

_____

_____

DRAW THE BABY

CAN YOU GUESS WHAT THE BABY IS GOING TO LOOK LIKE?

 # ADVICE FOR PARENTS

_____

_____

WISHES FOR BABY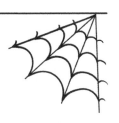

_____

_____

_____

 GUEST   GIFT

_____
_____
_____
_____
_____
_____
_____
_____
_____
_____
_____

_____
_____
_____
_____
_____
_____
_____
_____
_____
_____
_____

 GUEST   GIFT

_____   _____

_____   _____

_____   _____

_____   _____

_____   _____

_____   _____

_____   _____

_____   _____

_____   _____

_____   _____

_____   _____

 GUEST   GIFT

_____

_____

_____

_____

_____

_____

_____

_____

_____

_____

 # GUEST   # GIFT

_____   _____

_____   _____

_____   _____

_____   _____

_____   _____

_____   _____

_____   _____

_____   _____

_____   _____

_____   _____

_____   _____

GUEST

GIFT

_____

_____

_____

_____

_____

_____

_____

_____

_____

_____

_____

_____

GUEST

GIFT

_____ _____

_____ _____

_____ _____

_____ _____

_____ _____

_____ _____

_____ _____

_____ _____

_____ _____

_____ _____

_____ _____

 # GUEST   # GIFT

_____

_____

_____

_____

_____

_____

_____

_____

_____

_____

 # GUEST

GIFT

_____

_____

_____

_____

_____

_____

_____

_____

_____

_____

_____

 GUEST   GIFT

_____   _____

_____   _____

_____   _____

_____   _____

_____   _____

_____   _____

_____   _____

_____   _____

_____   _____

_____   _____

_____   _____

_____   _____

 GUEST   GIFT

_____   _____

_____   _____

_____   _____

_____   _____

_____   _____

_____   _____

_____   _____

_____   _____

_____   _____

_____   _____

# GUEST

GIFT

_____

_____

_____

_____

_____

_____

_____

_____

_____

_____

_____

_____

_____

_____

_____

_____

_____

_____

GUEST

GIFT

_____ _____

_____ _____

_____ _____

_____ _____

_____ _____

_____ _____

_____ _____

_____ _____

_____ _____

_____ _____

_____ _____

 GUEST   GIFT

_____   _____

_____   _____

_____   _____

_____   _____

_____   _____

_____   _____

_____   _____

_____   _____

_____   _____

_____   _____

GUEST

GIFT

_____ _____
_____ _____
_____ _____
_____ _____
_____ _____
_____ _____
_____ _____
_____ _____
_____ _____
_____ _____

 GUEST   GIFT

_____   _____

_____   _____

_____   _____

_____   _____

_____   _____

_____   _____

_____   _____

_____   _____

_____   _____

_____   _____

_____   _____

 GUEST   GIFT

_____   _____

_____   _____

_____   _____

_____   _____

_____   _____

_____   _____

_____   _____

_____   _____

_____   _____

_____   _____

_____   _____

 GUEST

GIFT

_____

_____

_____

_____

_____

_____

_____

_____

_____

_____

_____

_____

_____

_____

_____

_____

_____

_____

_____

_____

GUEST

GIFT

_____   _____

_____   _____

_____   _____

_____   _____

_____   _____

_____   _____

_____   _____

_____   _____

_____   _____

_____   _____

_____   _____

 # GUEST # GIFT

 # GUEST 👻 # 🍬 GIFT 🍬

_____   _____

_____   _____

_____   _____

_____   _____

_____   _____

_____   _____

_____   _____

_____   _____

_____   _____

_____   _____

_____   _____

_____   _____

HAPPY MEMORIES

HAPPY MEMORIES

Happy Memories

HAPPY MEMORIES

HAPPY MEMORIES

HAPPY MEMORIES

HAPPY MEMORIES

HAPPY MEMORIES

HAPPY MEMORIES

HAPPY MEMORIES

Happy Memories

HAPPY MEMORIES

Happy memories

HAPPY MEMORIES

HAPPY MEMORIES

Happy Memories

HAPPY MEMORIES

Happy memories

Happy memories

Happy Memories

NOTES

NOTES

NOTES

NOTES

NOTES

NOTES

NOTES

NOTES

NOTES

Made in the USA
Coppell, TX
22 September 2022